Mother and Daughter

A lifetime of love
to be remembered and cherished.

A Record Book of Love
A Gift of Memories™

©1999 Havoc Publishing

ISBN 1-57977-130-0

Published by Havoc Publishing
San Diego, California

Design©1998 Jerianne Van Dijk

Please write to us for more information
on Havoc Publishing products.

Havoc Publishing
6330 Nancy Ridge Drive, Suite 104
San Diego, California 92121

Mother and Daughter

A Record Book For:

Nina   Lilly

Mama & Kanini

Contents

Contents

The Two of Us

Photograph

"Children are the anchors that hold a mother to life."

Sophocles

Mother

Name _Maria Soldanha_

Birth date _10th December, 1977_

Birth place _Bangalore_

Address _____

Other pertinent information _One older mother Niren Saldanha_

Daughter

Name _Nina Correa_

Birth date _22nd August 2014_

Birth place _USA_

Address _____

Other pertinent information _My Dad Mike Correa_

Traits and Characteristics

Physical similarities _____

_____

_____

_____

_____

_____

Ways we are different _____

_____

_____

_____

_____

_____

We're So Alike

The first time I noticed we were alike _____

_____

_____

_____

Things you say that I say _____

_____

_____

_____

Things you do that I do _____

_____

_____

_____

Photograph

"Only mothers can think of the future-because
they give birth to it in their children."

Maxim Gorky

Interesting Characteristics

Things about us that are unconventional _____

_____

_____

_____

_____

What I think is special about you _____

_____

_____

_____

_____

All in a Day

Our typical day_____

_____

_____

_____

_____

The most important things we do_____

_____

_____

_____

_____

Our traditional roles_____

_____

_____

_____

_____

_____

Our non-traditional roles_____

_____

_____

_____

_____

_____

Our Family

Photograph

"Romance fails us and so do friendships, but the relationship of
parent and child, less noisy than all others, remains indelible and
indestructible, the strongest relationship on earth."

Theodor Reik

Photo

Name_____

Birth date _____

Photo

Name_____

Birth date _____

Photo

Name_____

Birth date _____

Photo

Name_____

Birth date _____

Home Sweet Home

Where I live_____

_____

_____

What makes it special_____

_____

_____

My decorating style_____

_____

_____

Projects still to be done_____

_____

Where You Live_____

_____

_____

What makes it special_____

_____

_____

_____

_____

The best household tips you've given me_____

_____

_____

_____

Photograph

Photograph

Triumphs and Successes

My greatest achievements are_____

_____

_____

_____

_____

I think your greatest achievements are_____

_____

_____

_____

_____

_____

My proudest moment with you was_____

_____

_____

_____

_____

_____

_____

_____

_____

_____

"Oh, what a power is motherhood, possessing a potent spell.
All women alike fight fiercely for a child."

Euripides

Our Own Traditions

Isn't it great the way we_____

_____

_____

_____

_____

_____

_____

_____

_____

Photograph

Comments of Affection

You have inspired me to_____

_____

_____

_____

I really admire you because_____

_____

_____

_____

_____

The best things you've done_____
_____
_____
_____
_____

What I love most about you_____
_____
_____
_____
_____
_____

I'm Glad We're Friends

I'm glad we're friends because _____

_____

_____

_____

_____

_____

_____

_____

Things I'm glad we can share_____

_____

_____

_____

_____

_____

I love it when we_____

_____

_____

_____

_____

Photograph

Photograph

Across the Generations

I love your youthful approach to_____

_____

_____

_____

_____

Ways you stay young_____

_____

_____

_____

What I like about getting older_____

_____

_____

_____

_____

What I appreciate now that I didn't appreciate before_____

_____

_____

_____

_____

_____

"We never know the love of our parents for us
till we have become parents."
Henry Ward Beecher

Secrets
We Keep

I never told you about the time _____

_____

_____

_____

_____

_____

_____

_____

_____

_____

"Who takes the child by the hand, takes
the mother by the heart."

Danish Proverb

I can't believe you did that_____

_____

_____

_____

_____

_____

You kept my secret so well the time_____

_____

_____

_____

_____

Funniest Moments

Things that always make us laugh _____

_____

_____

_____

_____

Remember laughing about _____

_____

_____

_____

_____

_____

How humor has helped us _____

_____

_____

_____

_____

_____

Favorite jokes or fun stories _____

_____

_____

_____

_____

Photograph

Photograph

Simple Pleasures

Our happiest times _____

_____

_____

_____

_____

Favorite ways to relax _____

_____

_____

_____

_____

_____

_____

Things we enjoy most_____

_____

_____

_____

All-time favorite things_____

_____

_____

_____

_____

Special hobbies & interests we share_____

_____

_____

_____

_____

Fashion Statements

My favorite fashions then _Girlie Girl._
Nina the Daughter

My favorite fashions now

Your favorite fashions then _____

_____

_____

_____

_____

Your favorite fashions now _____

_____

_____

_____

_____

Photograph

Photograph

The World As It Was

How the world has changed_____

_____

_____

_____

Hot political issues_____

_____

_____

How my views of the world have changed_____

_____

_____

_____

World events that have affected us_____

_____

_____

_____

_____

_____

Environmental issues_____

_____

_____

_____

_____

_____

_____

Spring

Our favorite things to do in Spring _____

_____

_____

_____

_____

_____

Holidays, special events and trips together _____

_____

_____

_____

_____

Summer

Our favorite things to do in Summer_____

_____

_____

_____

_____

_____

Holidays, special events and trips together_____

_____

_____

_____

Fall

Our favorite things to do in Fall _____

_____

_____

_____

_____

_____

Holidays, special events and trips together _____

_____

_____

_____

_____

Winter

Our favorite things to do in Winter_____

_____

_____

_____

_____

Holidays, special events and trips together_____

_____

_____

_____

Photograph

Photograph

Best Advice

Best advice you've given me _____

_____

_____

_____

_____

_____

_____

_____

_____

_____

Fun Time

Best evening out together _____

_____

_____

_____

My favorite way to spend a day with you _____

_____

_____

_____

_____

_____

_____

Food For Thought

Mealtime favorites_____

_____

_____

_____

_____

Favorite family recipes_____

_____

_____

_____

_____

_____

Cooking fiascos_____

_____

_____

_____

_____

_____

Cooking tips and tricks_____

_____

_____

_____

_____

Our Favorite Recipes

Women We Admire

Women who have influenced my life _____

_____

_____

Who has influenced my life the most _____

_____

_____

How you inspire me _____

_____

_____

_____

Photograph

Travel and Adventures

Favorite trip together_____

_____

_____

_____

_____

_____

Most memorable moment on a trip together_____

_____

_____

_____

_____

Best travel story _____

_____

_____

_____

_____

Best road trip _____

_____

_____

_____

Farthest place traveled _____

_____

_____

_____

Hopes, Wishes and Dreams

For me _____

_____

_____

_____

_____

_____

_____

_____

_____

_____

For you _____

_____

_____

_____

_____

_____

_____

"There lay the little miracle among the pillows: so well
formed, so encompassed, as it were, with the harmony of
sweet proportions, with little hands that even then, though so
much tinier, were beautiful as now, with wide-open eyes blue
as the sky and brighter than the sunshine-and almost in that
very second he felt himself captured and held fast."

Thomas Mann

Available Record Books from Havoc

Baby	Mom
Coach	Mothers & Daughters
College Life	My Pregnancy
Couples	Our Honeymoon
Dad	Retirement
Family	School Days
Forever Friends	Single Life
Girlfriends	Sisters
Golf	Teacher
Grandmother	Traveling Adventures
Grandparents	Tying the Knot

Please write to us with your ideas for
additional Havoc Publishing products

Havoc Publishing
6330 Nancy Ridge Drive, Suite 104
San Diego, CA 92121